SCRIBNER READING SERIES

JOIN THE CIRCLE

Jack Cassidy

Doris Roettger   *Karen K. Wixson*

SCRIBNER EDUCATIONAL PUBLISHERS

New York

ACKNOWLEDGMENT
Portions of this text have been adapted from materials
originally prepared under the direction of Dr. Charles Walcutt
and Dr. Glenn McCracken.

ILLUSTRATIONS
Cover: Cheryl Griesbach & Stanley Martucci.
Jane Chambless-Rigie 23-25; Rick Cooley 55-57; Sal Murdocca 4-10,
44-49; Freya Tanz 11-22, 26-43, 50-54; Linda Weller 58-63.

SCRIBNER EDUCATIONAL PUBLISHERS
866 Third Avenue
New York, NY 10022
Collier Macmillan Publishers, London
Collier Macmillan Canada, Inc.

Printed in the United States of America
ISBN 0-02-256020-3
9 8 7 6 5

Contents

Sam

by Mike Thaler

5

8

A a

N n

an   an

Nan   Ann

R r

ran

Ann ran.
Nan ran.

13

D d

ran	an	Dad
Dan	and	add

Dad

Dad ran.
Ann ran.
Dad and Ann ran.

Dan ran.
Nan ran.
Dan and Nan ran.

15

U u

ran
run

Run, Run

Run, Nan.
Run, Dad.

Dad and Nan run.
Dad and Nan run and run.

17

Dan and Nan run.
Dan and Nan run to Dad.

Run, Dan.
Run, Nan.

Dan and Nan run.
Dan and Nan run and run.

M m

an   mad   drum
man   mud

Adam

Run, Nan.
Run, Ann.
Nan and Ann run to Adam.

Drum, Nan.

Drum, Ann.

Nan and Ann drum.

Adam and Nan and Ann drum.

Drum, drum, drum!

Drum, drum, drum!

The Drum

The  run to the drum.

The add to the drum.

The add and add to the drum.

23

The drum ran.

The drum ran and ran.

The drum ran to the mud.

The  add to the drum.

The  run the drum.

The  run the drum to the man.

Add to the

Dan and Adam add **2** .

Nan and Ann add **4** ● .

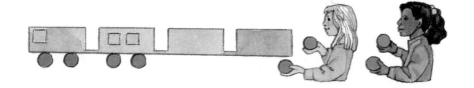

Dan and Adam add **4** ▫ .

Nan and Ann add I  and I .

Dan and Adam add I man and .

P p

pan	up	nap
pad	pup	map

ramp   dump

damp   pump

Up, Up, Up

Nan and the pup run.
Nan and the pup run up the ramp.
Up, up, up.

The pup and Nan run to Pam.

Pam and Nan pump.
Pam and Nan pump and pump.
Pam and Nan pump up the pad.
Up, up, up.

Nan and the pup nap.

I i

in	did	rip
pin	dip	drip

Pip and Nip

Pip and Nip run.
Pip and Nip run in the mud.

Pip and Nip run to Dan.
Pip and Nip drip and drip and drip.

Dan and Dad add to the pan.

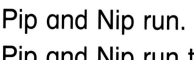

Pip and Nip run.
Pip and Nip run to the pan.
Pip and Nip dip into the pan.

Pip and Nip nap.
Pip and Nip nap in the pan.

Did Pip run in the mud?
Did Nip run to the pan?
Did Pip and Nip run to Dad?
Did Pip and Nip run to Dan?

S s

s in us

up	run	and	Dad
us	sun	sand	sad
Sis	rips	naps	miss
sips	dips	pumps	pass

s in is

is	runs	pins	spins

The Pup

Nan dips into the sand.
Sis naps in the sun.

The pup runs in the sand.
The pup runs and runs.

Nan and Sis miss the pup.
Nan is sad.

Did the pup pass us?
Did the pup pass the map?
Did the pup run to the man?

The pup runs in the sand.
The pup runs and runs.

The pup runs up to Nan.
Did the pup miss Nan?

Dan and Sid

The sun is up.
Dan runs.
Dan's pup runs.

Sid adds a map to the pad.

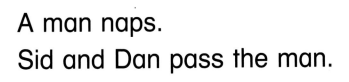

A man naps.
Sid and Dan pass the man.

Dan runs to a pump.
Sid and Dan pump and pump.
Dan's pup dips into a pan.

Sid pins up a pad.
Sid adds a pup to the pad.

Dan pins up a pad.
Dan adds a sun to the pad.

Sid and Dan miss the map.
Did the pup rip the map?

The pup runs to the pump.
Dan and Sid run to the pump.

Sid's map is in the mud.
Sid's map is damp.

43

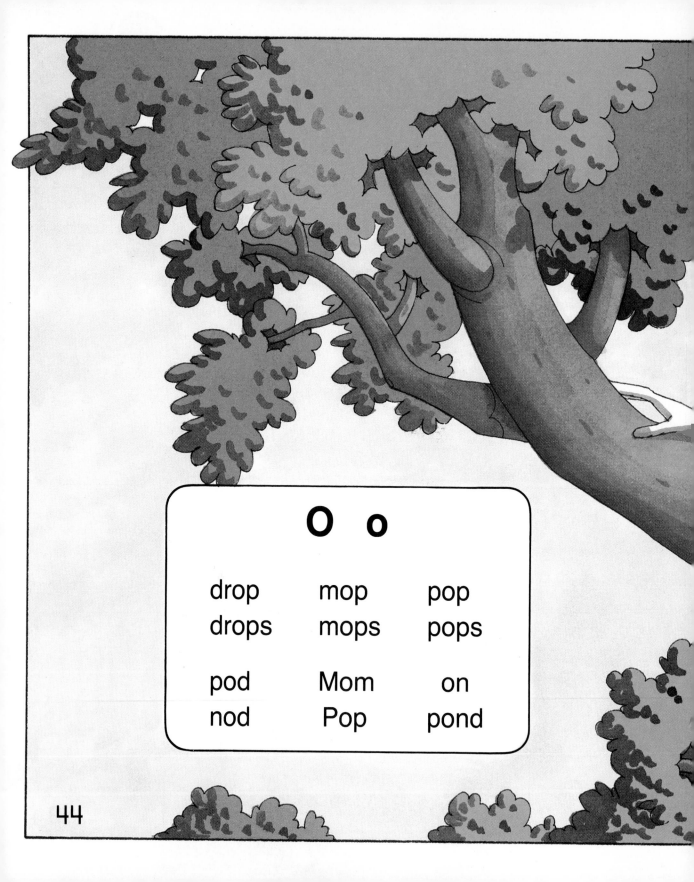

O o

drop	mop	pop
drops	mops	pops
pod	Mom	on
nod	Pop	pond

44

The Pond
by Mike Thaler

Sam runs.

Sam runs on Rumpus.
Rumpus is mad.

Sam runs into Pippin.
Pippin drops in the sand.
Pippin is mad.

Sam runs into Ronda.
Ronda drops in the mud.
Ronda is mad.

47

Sam runs!
Rumpus and Pippin and Ronda run!

48

Sam drops into the pond.

Is Rumpus mad?
Is Pippin mad?
Is Ronda mad?
Is Sam sad?

T t

at	sat	ant
it	sit	pants
tip	top	stand
trip	stop	stamp
not	dust	pass
spot	must	past

Go, Pat, Go!

Mom and Dad go to see Pat run.
Mom stands up.
Dad sits in the sun.

Mom and Dad see Pat.
Pat sees Mom and Dad.

51

A man stands up.
The man nods, GO!

Pat runs.
Tam and Matt run.

Pat's mom and dad stand up.
Go, Pat! Go!

Tam and Matt pass Pat.
Pat must not stop.
Pat must pass Tam and Matt.

Mom and Dad see Pat.
Pat runs past Mom and Dad.
Run, Pat! Run!

Pat runs and runs.
Pat must not trip.
Pat runs past Tam and Matt!

Tam and Matt stop.
Pat stops.

Mom and Dad run up to Pat.
Pat is tops!

The Damp Stamps

Drip, drip, drip.
Russ sees a damp spot.
Drip, drip, drip.
Russ runs!
Russ runs up to Mom and Dad.

Dad stops the drips.
Mom mops up.
Russ mops up.

55

A pad is damp.

Russ and Dad stand the pad up.

Russ sees a stamp on the pad.

The stamp is damp.

Dad sees a stamp on the pad.

Russ and Dad go to see
a stamp man.
Dad shows the stamps to the man.
The man nods at Dad.

The stamps go to the man.
The  go to Russ.

E e

pet	men	red	pep
net	ten	rest	step
set	tent	nest	steps

end	pen	mess
send	spend	dress
sent	spent	address

Moptop

Tess and Ted go to a show.
The show is in a tent.
The tent is red.

Tess spends a  .
Ted spends a .

Tess and Ted go into the tent.
Tess and Ted sit on the steps.

Into the tent run Moptop and Tramp.
Tramp is Moptop's pet.
Tramp is in pants.

Men set up ten steps.
Tramp must go up the ten steps.
Tramp must not stop.
At the top, Tramp sits and rests.

Tramp is a pest.
Tramp dumps sand on Moptop.

Tramp sets a trap.
Moptop trips.

Moptop rests on a mat.
Tramp sits on Moptop and taps.
Moptop's pet taps on a drum.
Tap, tap, tap.

61

Moptop is mad.
Moptop stands up and runs.

Tramp runs up a ramp.
Moptop runs up the ramp.

Moptop and Tramp drop.
Tramp pops up on Moptop.

Tramp runs up the steps.
Tramp runs to Tess.
Tess pets Tramp.

It is the end.
Tramp runs to Moptop.
The show is tops!

Story Vocabulary

Dad

Dad	15
Ann	
and	
Dan	
Nan	

Run, Run

to	18

Adam

Adam	21
drum	22

The Drum

the	23
add	

Up, Up, Up

ramp	29
Pam	
pump	30
pad	

Pip and Nip

Pip	33
Nip	
dip	34
into	

The Pup

pup	37
Sis	
miss	38
pass	
us	
map	

Dan and Sid

Dan's	40
Sid	
a	
pins	42
rip	
Sid's	43
damp	

The Pond

pond	45
Sam	46
Rumpus	
Pippin	47
Ronda	

Go, Pat, Go!

Pat	51
Mom	
go	
see	
nods	52
Tam	
Matt	
trip	54
tops	

The Damp Stamps

Russ	55
stamp	
shows	57

Moptop

Moptop	59
Tess	
Ted	
tent	
Tramp	60
pants	
set	
pest	61
dumps	

The comprehensive vocabulary list for JOIN THE CIRCLE includes the Story Vocabulary list and the words presented on the Phonics Skills pages in this book. A cumulative vocabulary list will be found in the Teacher's Edition.